MATH ON FIRE

MATCHSTICK MATHS

BY
JOHN DABELL

Book and CD ROM with single user license. Details of site license available from Millgate House.

MHPC

Millgate House
Publishing and Consultancy Ltd

Angel Solutions Ltd

Matchstick Maths

First published in Great Britain by Millgate House Publishing and
Consultancy Ltd, 2005

British Library Cataloguing in Publication Data
A record for this book is available from the British
Library

ISBN 978 0 9527506 3 5

Millgate House Publishing and Consultancy Ltd, Millgate House,
30 Mill Hill Lane, Sandbach, Cheshire, CW11 4PN, UK
www.millgatehouse.co.uk

Graphic Design by Kathryn Stawpert
Cover Illustration by Paul Muirehead
Type Design (puzzles) by Tom Murphy vii
CD by Angel Solutions, Liverpool

Printed by the Printing House Ltd, Marshfield Bank Employment Park,
Marshfield Bank, Crewe, Cheshire, CW2 8UY

Acknowledgements

I am indebted to Brenda Keogh and Stuart Naylor for bringing this book to life. Their outstanding support and faith has been an inspiration.

Thank you.

I dedicate this book to Wendy, my exceptional partner.

Contents

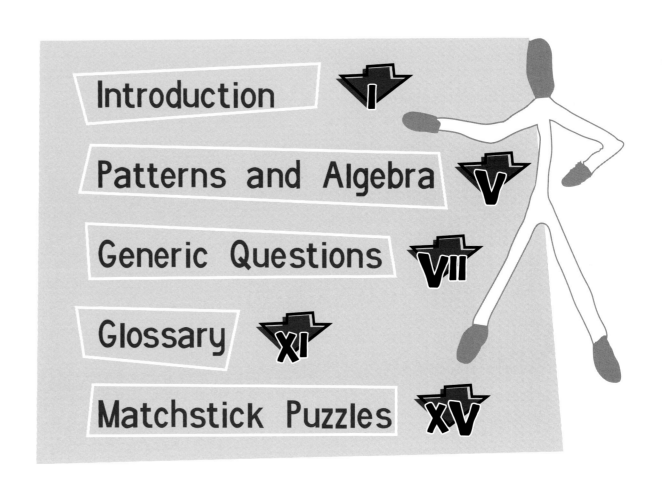

Introduction

What better way is there to **introduce** and **reinforce mathematical concepts** than **to make** them **fun** through **games, puzzles** and **problems to solve?**

Matchstick puzzles provide a rich resource for achieving curricular objectives in challenging and enjoyable ways.

Matchstick puzzles are a modest but effective kinaesthetic resource. They are particularly suitable for pupils in Key Stages 2 and 3, where they can have a positive impact on pupils' mathematical learning. Matchstick puzzles can be used to scaffold pupils' learning, offering a physical model of mathematical concepts. They are ideal for developing pupils' visualisation skills and for improving their knowledge and understanding of 2-D shape. They not only satisfy the need for practice and reinforcement of new learning, but also provide opportunities for the transfer of that knowledge to new contexts. Pupils typically find them highly motivating, including boys and girls from a range of backgrounds and with a variety of interests.

There are several reasons why you might decide to include these puzzles in your planning. Matchstick puzzles can be used to:

- improve concentration skills
- build confidence and self-reliance
- promote positive attitudes towards maths
- encourage co-operation and collaboration
- promote talk and discussion about mathematical ideas, using mathematical vocabulary
- provide a practical way to explore and explain mathematical concepts
- cultivate mathematical development by extending current knowledge and understanding
- cultivate thinking skills, flexibility and creativity
- improve mathematical thinking, including problem solving and investigative skills
- promote enjoyment of maths

As a practical resource matchsticks are readily available and inexpensive. They are easy to use, requiring little preparation in advance of a lesson. You might choose to fit matchstick puzzles into your teaching in a variety of ways, including:

- pupils working independently or collaboratively in groups
- as part of a whole class lesson or as a mental/oral starter or plenary
- as challenge or extension activities forming part of an enriched or accelerated curriculum e.g. learning algebra
- as an activity in a Maths Club
- as a homework activity to reinforce and extend learning
- as part of a display

The puzzles reflect a problem-solving philosophy and have been designed to challenge, entertain and inspire pupils into seeing maths in a new light . Although the puzzles demand a lot from pupils, they are not exclusively for high achievers. The puzzles can be done by most pupils, given appropriate support where necessary. You should use your discretion about how much help and support to provide, but your aim should be to enable pupils to work as independently as possible.

Using matchstick puzzles in your teaching

It is important to plan the puzzles carefully and to be clear about why you are using them. Since there are a number of ways that you might choose to use the matchstick puzzles (see above), it isn't possible to give definitive guidance about how to present them. However there are a number of general points that will be helpful to keep in mind.

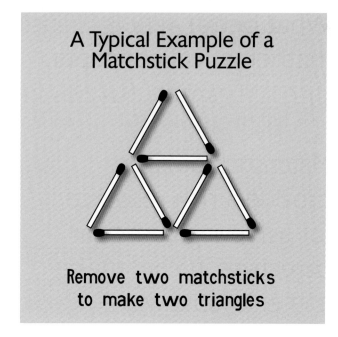

A Typical Example of a Matchstick Puzzle

Remove two matchsticks to make two triangles

Provide thinking time. Encourage pupils to sit back and think about what they might do before rushing into the problem.

Encourage collaboration. Even if they tackle the puzzles individually (e.g. for homework or as a lesson starter), talking through their ideas is a valuable part of the learning process.

Provide prompts and clues where necessary, in order to make connections and support lines of reasoning. If pupils are struggling after a few minutes you can suggest possible strategies or indicate one of the matchsticks that could be moved. Use higher-order questions such as 'What would happen if…?', 'I wonder why…?', and 'How can you tell that…?'

Create a positive learning environment in which all ideas are valued. This includes suspending judgement yourself and ensuring that pupils also show a positive attitude to other pupils' ideas.

Create a questioning climate. Praising thoughtful questions as much as imaginative suggestions helps to indicate how valuable questions can be.

Ask questions to get pupils thinking. Before pupils tackle the puzzle it is useful to ask questions about the initial shape. This helps to get them thinking creatively and can provide a starting point for tackling the puzzle. In the example shown above suitable questions could include the following:

How many triangles do you think there are?
(There are five – four small and one big triangle.)

What types of triangle can you see?
(They are equilateral or sometimes called acute angled triangles)

Can you define the type of triangle you have identified?
(A regular triangle – all sides are of equal length and all interior angles are the same size, i.e. 60 degrees. The shape can also be called a regular trigon.)

How many matchsticks make up the perimeter?

(Six)

How many matchsticks make up the interior?

(three)

How many matchsticks make up the exterior?

(six)

How many more matchsticks do you think you would need to make a score? What would be the shape name for that number?

(11 – hendecagon or undecagon)

Count the number of matchsticks - what type of a number do you think this is?

(Composite and square number)

You will see as you look through the range of puzzles that for many of the examples a set of generic questions can be helpful. An extensive list of possible generic questions is provided on pages vii-ix. Please don't use all the questions at the same time! There is also a glossary of mathematical terms and polygon names on pages xi - xiv that may come in useful when constructing puzzles and questions.

A perfect match

Recent research into learning reveals that many pupils have preferred learning styles. Some pupils have a visual dominance and prefer to learn by seeing; some have an auditory dominance and prefer to learn by hearing; while others have a kinaesthetic dominance and prefer to learn by doing. In a typical class in any subject in any school you are likely to find a broad mix of preferred learning styles.

Clearly it is important for all pupils to learn how to learn using a variety of strategies and styles. Nevertheless it is easy to see how some pupils could be systematically disadvantaged if a narrow range of learning styles is used. It is therefore necessary to teach mathematics using a range of learning styles to ensure that all learners are included.

Matchsticks lend themselves to all three learning styles and offer a balanced multi-sensory approach to learning. When using the matchstick activities pupils are actively engaged at all three levels. They are looking at the matchstick templates; listening to your instructions and scaffolding suggestions; and are solving puzzles by doing (including moving actual matchsticks around if necessary).

As the old proverb suggests:

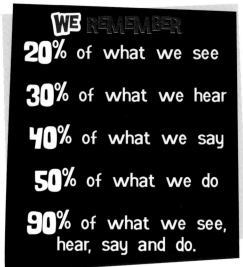

WE REMEMBER
20% of what we see
30% of what we hear
40% of what we say
50% of what we do
90% of what we see, hear, say and do.

Given this, matchstick puzzles really are a perfect match. They encompass all three learning preferences within enjoyable and challenging activities.

CAUTION

USING MATCHSTICKS MAY SET CHILDREN'S INTEREST IN MATHS ON FIRE!

DO NOT EXTINGUISH!

V+VI=XI

iv

Patterns and Algebra

After pupils have manipulated matchsticks to create new shapes you can challenge them further by using matchsticks to create patterns.

The following lesson plan shows you one possible approach.

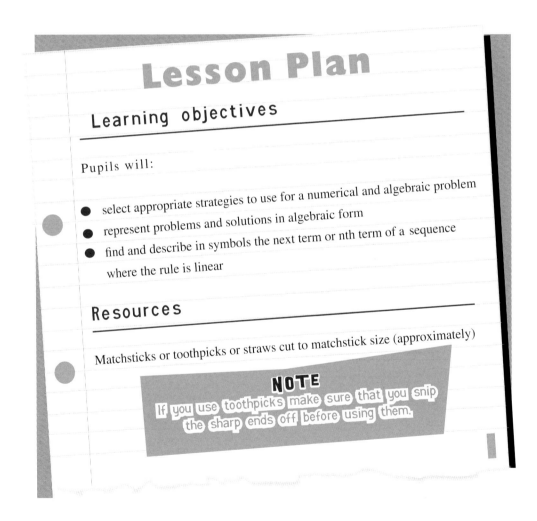

Lesson Plan

Learning objectives

Pupils will:

- select appropriate strategies to use for a numerical and algebraic problem
- represent problems and solutions in algebraic form
- find and describe in symbols the next term or nth term of a sequence where the rule is linear

Resources

Matchsticks or toothpicks or straws cut to matchstick size (approximately)

NOTE
If you use toothpicks make sure that you snip the sharp ends off before using them.

WHAT TO DO - LEARNING ACTIVITY

Look at the following growing pattern of triangular matchsticks.

How many matchsticks would be needed to make 20 triangles? 100 triangles?

Encourage pupils to solve this problem systematically by drawing a table. For example:

Number of triangles (t)	Number of matchsticks (m)
1	3
2	5
3	7
4	9

The table helps pupils to notice the following:

- 2 more matchsticks are needed for each additional triangle
- The sequence generated is 3, 5, 7, 9,11….

So a general rule for the number of matchsticks can be generated:

$$m = t \times 2 + 1 \qquad \text{or} \qquad m = 2t + 1$$

Therefore 20 triangles will need $20 \times 2 + 1 = 41$ matchsticks

Therefore 100 triangles will need $100 \times 2 + 1 = 201$ matchsticks

EXTENSION

Investigate other growing matchstick patterns. For example:

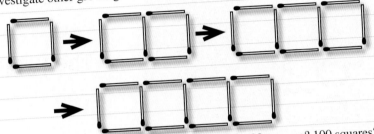

How many matchsticks would be needed to make 20 squares? 100 squares?

Encourage pupils to solve this problem systematically by drawing a table. For example:

Number of squares (s)	Number of matchsticks (m)
1	4
2	7
3	10
4	13

The table helps pupils to notice the following:

- 3 more matchsticks are needed for each additional square
- The sequence generated is 4, 7, 10 , 13, 16 ….

So a general rule for the number of matchsticks can be generated:

$$m = s \times 3 + 1 \qquad \text{or} \qquad m = 3s + 1$$

Therefore 20 squares will need $3 \times 2 + 1 = 61$ matchsticks

Therefore 100 squares will need $100 \times 3 + 1 = 301$ matchsticks

NOTE
There are proformas for patterns and algebra on the CD.

Generic Questions

Generic questions that may be useful with the matchstick puzzles.

Each of the matchstick maths puzzles comes with an associated problem.

The problems enable you to extend the pupils' learning, but it doesn't have to end there. It is possible to create more questions to make the most of the matchstick maths puzzles.

These questions provide additional challenges and maximise the pupils' learning. A nest of challenges can be fashioned, like a Russian stacking doll, so that pupils are introduced to new investigations and pushed further in their learning. The combination of puzzles, problems and questions provides you with an extensive resource for learning.

The use of astute and well-focused questions allows you to assess pupils' learning and address their misconceptions beyond the puzzle itself. The puzzles provide a stimulating context for pupils to extend their learning by generating their own questions.

The generic questions which follow are possible starting points for you to use as springboards into various aspects of the maths curriculum. They provide you and the pupils with the opportunity to explore their mathematical thinking and understanding of a range of concepts.

Questions

Have you noticed that ….?

What would happen if…?

I wonder why…?

I wonder whether….?

Suppose that we….?

Do you think that….?

How can you tell that…?

Are you able to….?

Can you see another way to….?

Is there another way that you could….?

Questions

How many different kinds of shapes do you think you can see?

How many triangles/squares/rectangles/etc can you see?

How many matchsticks make up the perimeter?

How many matchsticks make up the interior?

Can you write the total number of matches in Roman numerals?

Can you round the total number of matches to the nearest 10?

Is the total number of matchsticks greater than or less than a…..(e.g. baker's dozen, score, etc)?

Questions

Count the exterior number of matches. How many more would you need to make 50? 100? 1,000? 10,000?

Count the number of matchsticks – do you think the number is a prime? composite? square? triangular?

Count the matchsticks. How many more matchsticks do you think you would need to make the 7th multiple of….?

Count the matchsticks. What are the factors of this number?

What is the product of the interior and exterior matches?

Questions

Do you think the shape shown will tessellate?

Do you think any of the matches are parallel to each other?

Do you think any of the matches are perpendicular to each other?

Count the matchsticks. What is the name of a polygon with that number of sides?

Count the number of matchsticks. What is the name of a polyhedron with that number of faces?

How many right angles can you see in the shape?

Questions

How many lines of reflective symmetry do you think you can see?

What is the rotational order of symmetry?

Do you think any of the shapes shown are congruent?

With the exterior representing units and the interior representing the tenths, can you write the number of matches as a decimal?

What is the total number of matches multiplied by eight (change to a chosen number) more than the third prime number (change to square, composite etc)?

Questions

Is the number of matches shown a factor of…. (e.g. 32, 49, etc)?

Can you write the interior and exterior matches as a fraction/ proportion/ratio?

Write the interior and exterior as a set of Cartesian co-ordinates. Which number is the ordinate?

What is the quotient of the exterior divided by the interior?

Can you express the number of matches shown as an abstract number?

Can you express the number of matches shown as a concrete number?

X

Glossary

This A-Z of key concepts will be useful in helping you to create your own matchstick puzzle problems.

A

Acute Describes angles between 0 and 90 degrees.

Adjacent Adjoining (as used to describe lines and angles).

Alternate Every other one in a sequence.

Angle The number of degrees rotated around a point.

Area The amount of space within a perimeter (expressed in square units).

Ascending Order The arrangement of numbers from smallest to largest.

Average A number representing a set of numbers (obtained by dividing the total value of the numbers by the number of items).

Axis of symmetry A line dividing a shape into two symmetrical parts.

B

Baker's dozen The name given to the number 13.

Base The line or face on which a shape is standing.

Base angles Those angles adjacent to the base of a shape.

Bisect To divide into two equal parts.

Breadth Another name for width. It is the distance across from side to side.

C

Capacity The amount of space in the interior of an object (the amount of liquid/air it contains).

Cardinal number A number that shows quantity but not order.

Carroll diagram A problem-solving diagram used in classification activities.

Circumference The distance around a circle (its perimeter).

Composite number A number with more than two factors.

Congruent Congruent shapes are the same shape and size (equal).

Consecutive Consecutive numbers follow in order without interruption (e.g. 2,3,4,5).

Coordinates Numbers used to locate a point on a grid.

D

Denominator The number below the line in a fraction.

Descending order The arrangement of numbers from the largest to smallest.

Diagonal A straight line connecting two non-adjacent vertices (corners) of a polygon.

Difference	By how much a number is bigger or smaller than another.	**G** **Greater than**	An inequality between numbers. The symbol used to represent greater than is a right facing arrow before the smaller number e.g. 8 > 3.	**K** **Kite**	A quadrilateral that has two adjacent pairs of sides that are equal in length, and at least one pair of opposite angles are equal.

Difference — By how much a number is bigger or smaller than another.

Digit — Any number from 0 to 9 (inclusive).

Digital root — The digital root of 58 is 4 because 5 + 8 = 13 and 1 + 3 = 4.

Dimensions — The measurements of a shape (i.e. length, width, height).

Dodecagon — A twelve sided polygon.

E

Edge — The intersection of two faces of a three-dimensional object.

Enneakaidecagon (enneadecagon) — A polygon with nineteen sides and nineteen angles.

Equation — A statement of equality between two expressions (e.g. 3 × 4 = 6 + 6).

Equilateral triangle — A triangle with congruent (equal) sides and angles.

Even number — A positive or negative number exactly divisible by 2.

Exterior — Outside.

F

Face — A plane surface of a three-dimensional object.

Face value — The numeral itself despite its position in a number (e.g. the face value of 8 in 38,250 is 8).

Factor — A number which will divide exactly into another number.

G

Greater than — An inequality between numbers. The symbol used to represent greater than is a right facing arrow before the smaller number e.g. 8 > 3.

Gross — The name given to the number 144.

H

Hendecagon — A two dimensional shape with eleven sides and eleven angles, also called an undecagon.

Heptagon — A two dimensional shape with seven sides and seven angles, also called a septagon.

Hexagon — A polygon with six sides.

Horizontal — Describes a line or plane parallel to the earth's surface.

I

Improper fraction — A fraction whose numerator is equal to or greater than its denominator.

Integer — A negative or positive whole number.

Interior — Inside.

Intersection — The point or line where two lines or two faces meet.

Irregular shapes — Shapes which do not have all congruent sides and all congruent angles.

Isosceles triangle — A triangle which has two equal sides of equal length.

K

Kite — A quadrilateral that has two adjacent pairs of sides that are equal in length, and at least one pair of opposite angles are equal.

L

Less than — An inequality between numbers. The symbol used to represent less than is a left facing arrow after the smaller number e.g. 5 < 10.

Line of symmetry — (See axis of symmetry).

Lozenge — Another name for a rhombus.

M

Mean — The average of a set of numbers. The sum of the values in a set of data divided by the total number of items in that set.

Median — The middle value of a set of ordered data.

Mode — The value that occurs the most often in a set of data.

Multiple — The product of a given number with another factor.

N

Nonagon — A polygon with nine sides and nine angles.

Numerator — The number above the line in a fraction.

O

Oblique — Sloping or slanting.

Oblong — A shape with two pairs of straight, unequal sides and four right angles. Also known as a rectangle.

Obtuse angle — An angle between 90 and 180 degrees.

Octagon — A polygon with eight sides and eight angles.

Odd number — A number which leaves a remainder of one when divided by two.

Ordinal number — Describes a position in a number sequence e.g. 2nd

P

Parallel lines — Lines with no common points and always the same distance apart.

Parallelogram — A four-sided polygon with opposite sides equal and parallel and the opposite angles are equal in size.

Perimeter — The length of the distance around the boundary of a shape.

Perpendicular line — A line at right angles to another line or plane.

Polyhedron — A three dimensional shape with plane faces.

Place value — Indicates the position of a numeral (e.g. the place value of the 3 in 738 is 30).

Prime number — A number with only two factors, 1 and itself (e.g. 2, 3, 5, 7, 11, 13, 17, 19, 23…).

Product — The result when two or more numbers are multiplied.

Q

Quadrant — A quarter of the area of a circle which also contains a right angle.

Quotient — The result when one number is divided by another number.

Quindecagon — A polygon with fifteen sides and fifteen angles.

R

Rectangle — A quadrilateral with opposite sides equal and parallel and containing four right angles. Also known as an oblong.

Reflex angle — An angle greater than 180 degrees.

Rhombus — A parallelogram with congruent sides. Opposite sides are parallel and opposite sides are equal in size.

Roman numerals — Seven letters are used in combination to write numbers:

I – 1   V – 5   X – 10
L – 50   C – 100   D – 500
M – 1000

Rotational symmetry — A shape is said to have rotational symmetry if it looks the same in different positions when rotated about its centre.

Rounding — An approximation used to express a number in a more convenient way.

S

Scalene triangle — A triangle that has three sides of different length and no equal angles.

Score — The name given to the number 20.

Septagon — A polygon with seven sides and seven angles.

Squared — A number squared is a number multiplied by itself.

Square number — A number whose units can be arranged into a square (e.g. 1, 4, 9, 16, 25, 36, 49, 64…).

Sum — The result when two or more numbers are added together.

Symmetrical — A shape is symmetrical if it is identical on either side of a line dividing it into two parts.

T

Tally — A record of items using vertical and oblique lines to represent each item.

Tetragon — A four sided shape.

Tessellation	Shapes fitted together with a number of exact copies and with no overlaps or gaps.
Translation	Takes place when a shape is moved from one place to another just by sliding it (without rotating, reflecting or enlarging).
Trapezium	A quadrilateral with two parallel sides.
Triangular number	A number whose units can be arranged into a triangle (e.g. 1, 3, 6, 10, 15, 21 …) e.g. fourth triangular number = 10.

Trigon	A three sided shape.
Vertex	The point at which two or more line segments or two or more edges of a polyhedron meet.
Vertical line	A line which is at right angles to a horizontal line.

NAMING POLYGONS

3	triangle (trigon)	17	heptadecagon (heptakaidecagon)
4	quadrilateral (tetragon)	18	octadecagon (octakaidecagon)
5	pentagon	19	enneadecagon (enneakaidecagon)
6	hexagon	20	icosagon
7	heptagon	30	triacontagon
8	octagon	40	tetracontagon
9	nonagon (enneagon)	50	pentacontagon
10	decagon	60	hexacontagon
11	hendecagon (undecagon)	70	heptacontagon
12	dodecagon	80	octacontagon
13	tridecagon (triskaidecagon)	90	enneacontagon
14	tetradecagon (tetrakaidecagon)	100	hectogon
15	pentadecagon (pentakaidecagon)	1000	chiliagon
16	hexadecagon (hexakaidecagon)	10000	myriagon

For more information and a more comprehensive list about the naming of polygons go to the following web site:

mathforum.org/dr.math/

Matchstick Puzzles

In this section you will find the Maths on Fire matchstick puzzles. Each page has an innovative layout to help you to use them creatively in your teaching.

You will find it helpful to read the information below before you start to use the puzzles.

On each page you will find:

An additional question to challenge pupils to think about another aspect of mathematics relating to the puzzle.

Answer to the additional question.

A solution to the puzzle. In some cases the solution has been rotated through 90° in order to fit the solution into the space available. **NB** There may be more than one solution to each problem.

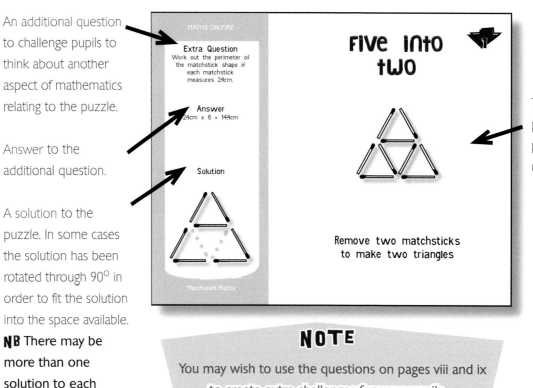

The matchstick puzzle that can be photocopied for use by pupils.

NOTE

You may wish to use the questions on pages viii and ix to create extra challenges for your pupils.

The book and CD ROM can be used in complementary ways.

a) Using the book

The book has been designed to enable you to photocopy the puzzle without including the solution (see Figure 1). The page layout makes it easy to copy part of the page rather than the whole page. Your photocopy will have the matchstick puzzle with a blank working area below it, so pupils can use the blank area to sketch out possible solutions.

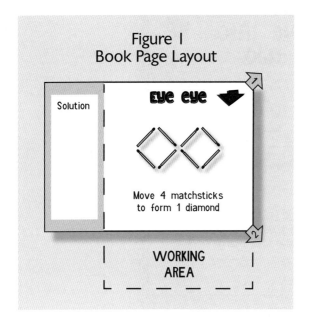

Figure 1
Book Page Layout

Solution

eye eye

Move 4 matchsticks
to form 1 diamond

**WORKING
AREA**

NOTE
(Work sheets can also be printed from
the PDF file on the CD ROM.)

Different photocopiers vary in the way that you position a document for copying. Figures 2A and 2B show you how to place the book to copy just the puzzle. NB You may need to cover part of the glass platen on the photocopier with a piece of white paper so that the blank working area on the copy is white rather than black.

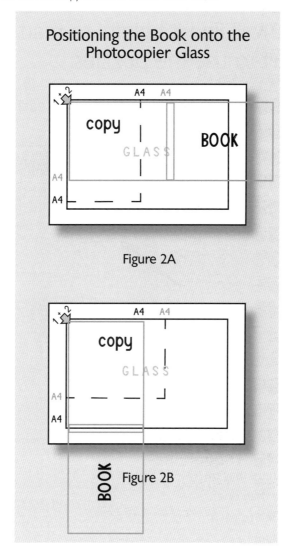

Positioning the Book onto the Photocopier Glass

A4   A4

copy

GLASS   BOOK

A4

A4

Figure 2A

A4   A4

copy

GLASS

A4

A4

BOOK Figure 2B

An overhead projector (OHP) can be used to present the problem to a class, though it is helpful if they have the photocopy to work on as well. You can use overlays and coloured pens to test out possible solutions with the class. Younger and less confident pupils will find it helpful to make the problem more tangible by using actual matchsticks.

b) Using the CD ROM

Please read the 'readme.doc' on the CD ROM
before using any of the interactive files.

You can make use of the CD software to present the problem, test out possible solutions and create new matchstick puzzles. The CD is set up so that the matchsticks can be moved around, dragging, dropping and rotating individual matchsticks as necessary. The text on the note pad can be changed or erased.

The matchbox allows matches to be added or removed, new puzzles to be created and extra solutions found. The CD also contains proformas for patterns and algebra. There is a 'blank canvas' page added to enable new puzzles to be made.

If you have a data projector attached to a computer then the whole class can see what happens as a result of moving the matchsticks. Ideally pupils can demonstrate possible solutions to the class. If you have a site license for the CD then you might do this in a computer suite, with pupils working at their own computers.

You should also be able to use whiteboard software to move matchsticks around to test out possible solutions.

PUZZLE INDEX

xvii

Extra Question

Work out the perimeter of the matchstick shape if each matchstick measures 2.4cm.

Answer

2.4cm x 6 = 14.4cm

Solution

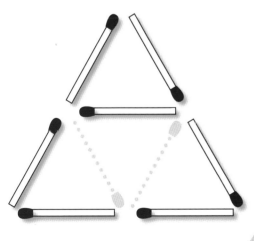

Five into two

Remove two matchsticks to make two triangles

2

Testing triangles

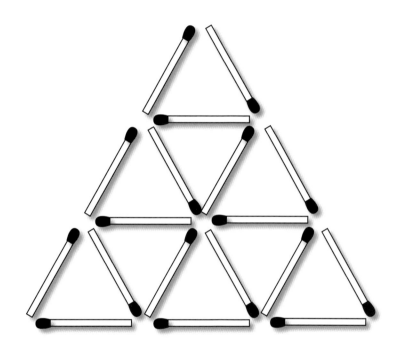

© J Dabell 2005

Remove 4 matchsticks to make 5 triangles

Extra Question

Multiply the number of matchsticks on the interior by the number of matchsticks on the exterior.

Answer

9 x 9 = 81

Solution

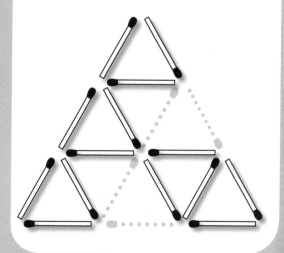

Trying trigons

Extra Question

Is the number of matchsticks to be moved a composite number or a prime number?

Answer

5 matches have to be moved. 5 is a prime number because it has only two factors, 1 and itself.

Solution

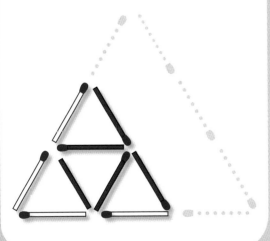

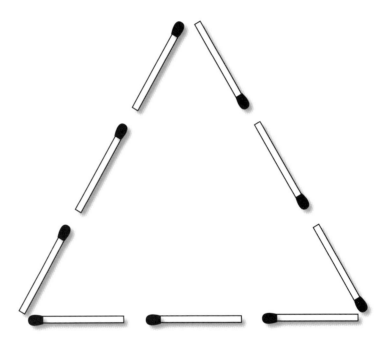

Move 5 matchsticks to make 5 triangles

EYES CLOSED

Extra Question

Is the total number of matchsticks greater than or less than a baker's dozen?

Answer

Less than because a baker's dozen is 13.

© J Dabell 2005

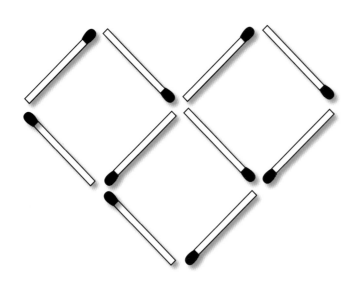

Solution

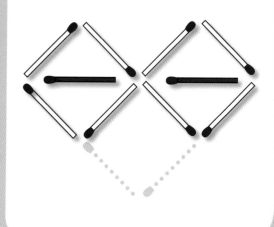

Move 2 matchsticks to make 4 triangles

Eye Eye

Extra Question

By what other name is a diamond known?

Answer

Rhombus, parallelogram and lozenge.

Solution

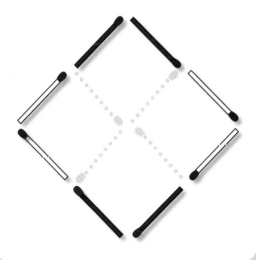

Move 4 matchsticks to form 1 diamond

Quadrant

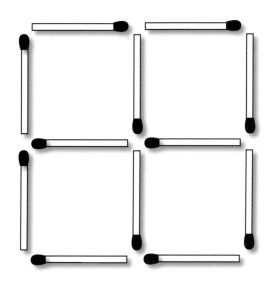

© J Dabell 2005

Move 2 matchsticks to make 7 squares

Extra Question

Multiply the number of interior matchsticks by the number of horizontal exterior matchsticks and subtract this from the number of degrees in a circle (four quadrants).

Answer

4 x 4 = 16
360 - 16 = 344

Solution

Extra Question

Count the matchsticks and then subtract a score.

Answer

24 - 20 = 4

Solution

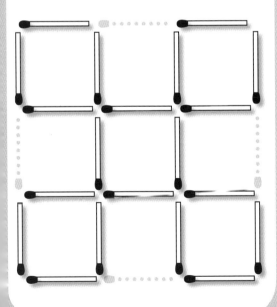

square five

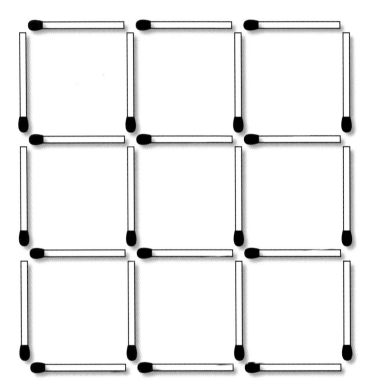

Remove 4 matchsticks to leave 5 squares

Cross

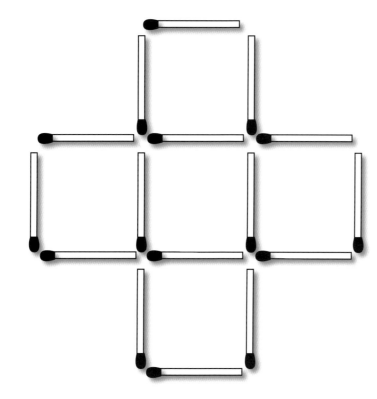

Move 4 matchsticks to form 3 squares

© J Dabell 2005

Extra Question

Multiply the number of vertical matches by the number of horizontal matches then divide by the number of interior matches.

Answer

8 x 8 = 64

64 ÷ 4 = 16

Solution

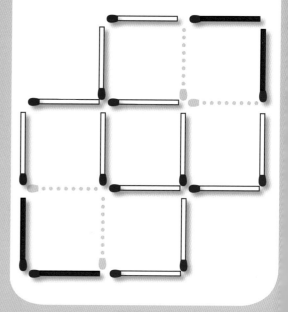

Extra Question

Add the number of matchsticks to the position L appears in the alphabet then find the digital root.

Answer

16 + 12 = 28
2 + 8 = 10
1 + 0 = 1

Solution

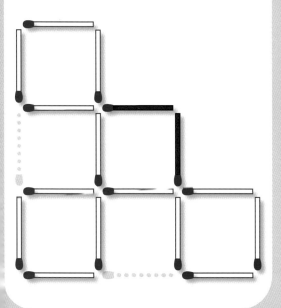

Learner

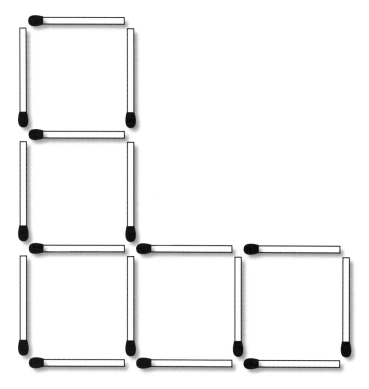

Move 2 matchsticks to form 4 squares

Three to three

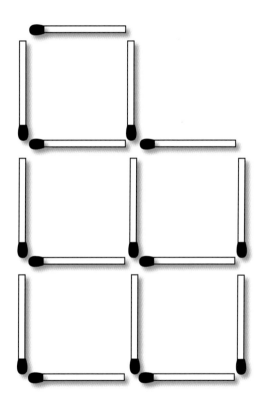

Remove 3 matchsticks to form 3 squares

Extra Question

Add a baker's dozen to the number of matches that make up the shape then multiply by the number of right-angles in a square.

Answer

13 (baker's dozen) + 15 = 28

28 x 4 = 112

Solution

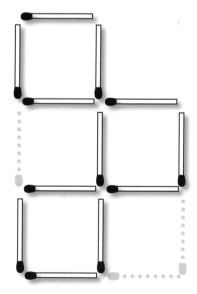

© J Dabell 2005

Extra Question

Count the number of oblongs that make up the shape and multiply by the number of horizontal matches.

Answer

There are 3 oblongs.

3 x 7 = 21

Solution

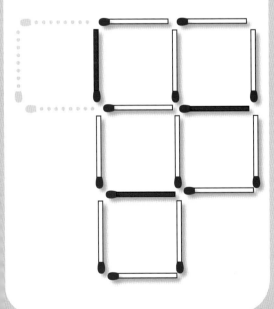

six squares

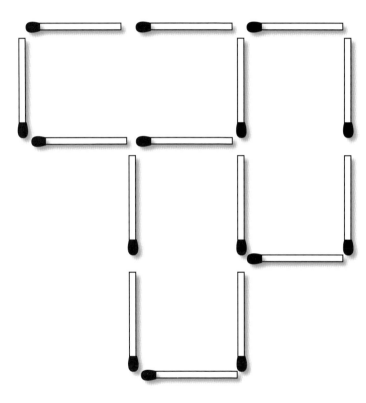

© J Dabell 2005

Move 3 matchsticks to form 6 squares

Identical squares

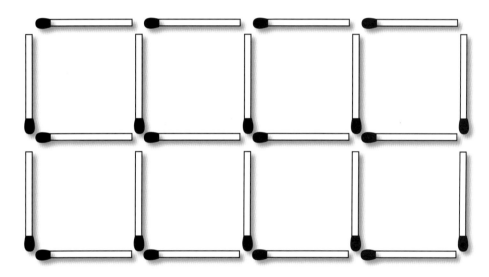

© J Dabell 2005

Remove 6 matchsticks to form 4 congruent squares

Extra Question

Multiply the horizontal matches by the interior matches and then subtract the total number of right-angles you can see.

Answer

12 x 10 = 120
120 - 32 = 88

Solution

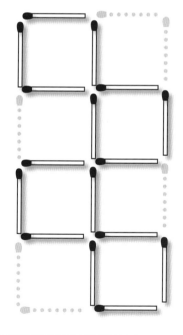

Congruent L's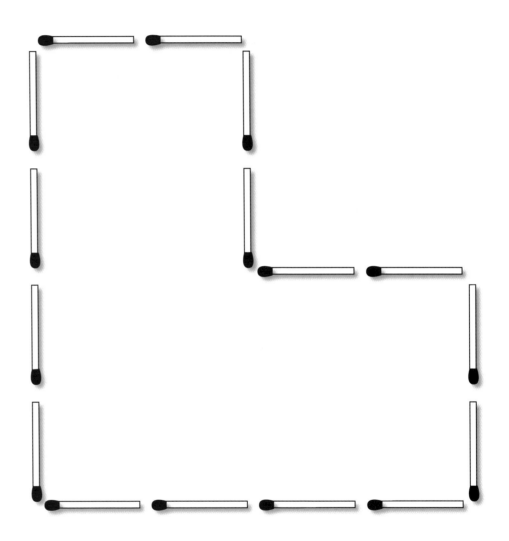

13

Extra Question

Divide the total number of matches by the first prime number.

Answer

16 ÷ 2 = 8

Solution

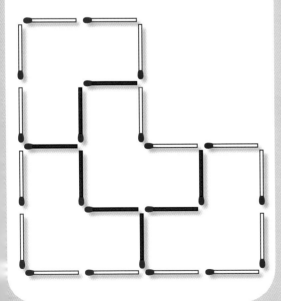

Add 8 matchsticks to form 4 congruent L-shapes

14

square and son

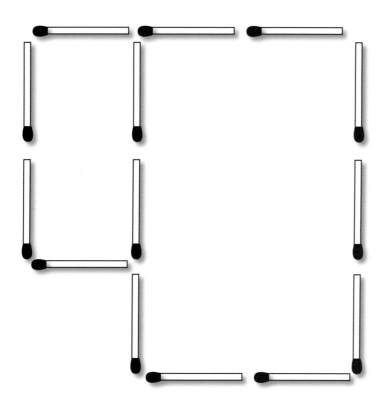

Move 2 matchsticks to form 2 squares

Extra Question

Halve the number of matches then add the fifth square number.

Answer

14 ÷ 2 = 7
7 + 25 = 32

Solution

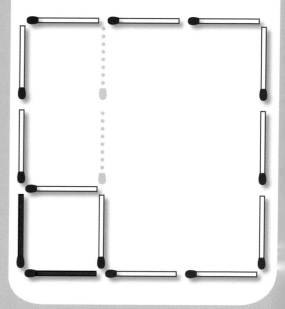

Extra Question

Add the number of sides in two nonagons to the number of horizontal matches then find the digital root.

Answer

$9 + 9 = 18$

$18 + 6 = 24$

$2 + 4 = 6$

Solution

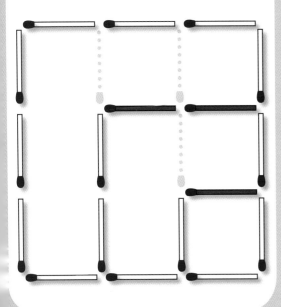

Three square

15

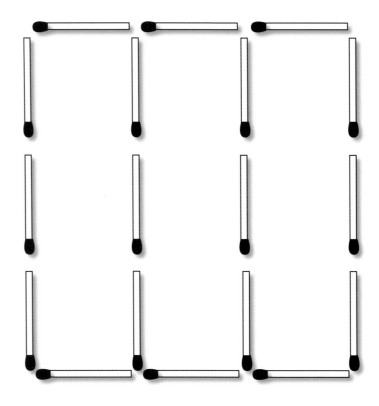

© J Dabell 2005

Move 3 matchsticks to make 3 squares

square path

16

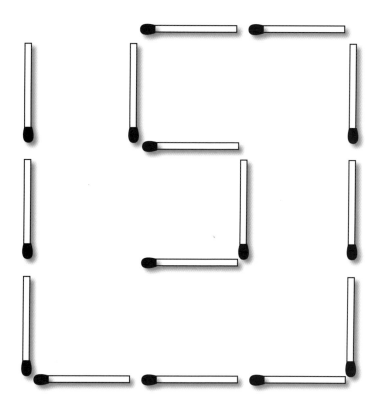

Move 2 matchsticks
to form 2 squares

Extra Question

Add the number of sides in
a quindecagon to one third
the number of matches.

Answer

15 (quindecagon sides)
+ 5 = 20 (a score)

Solution

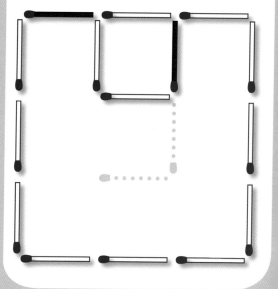

© J Dabell 2005

square up

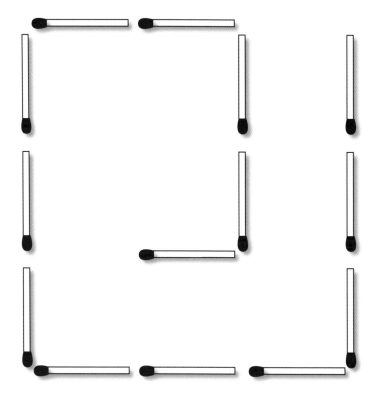

Move 2 matchsticks to make 2 squares

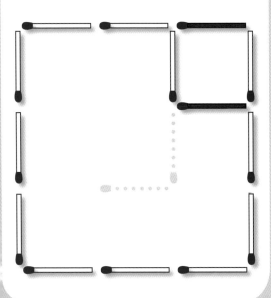

Extra Question

Subtract the number of sides in a heptagon from the total number of matches.

Answer

14 - 7 (heptagon) = 7

Solution

Three L's

18

© J Dabell 2005

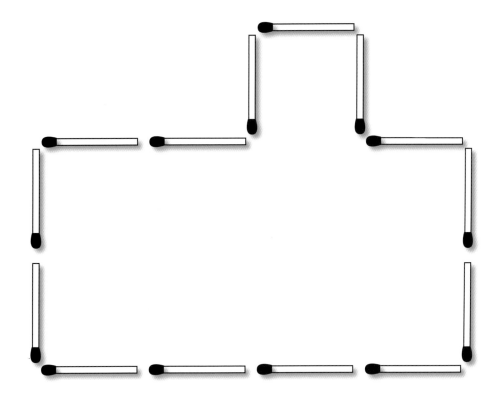

Add 5 matchsticks
to form 3 congruent shapes

Extra Question

Quadruple the number of matches then subtract this from a gross.

Answer

4 x 14 = 56

144 (a gross) - 56 = 88

Solution

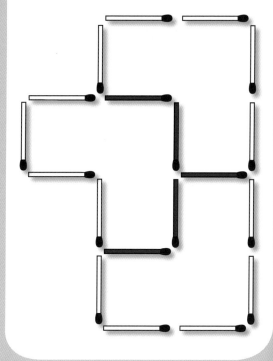

Extra Question

Multiply the number of oblique matches by the number of mm in 1cm.

Answer

10 oblique matches x 10 = 100

Solution

VIEW FROM HERE

keep fit

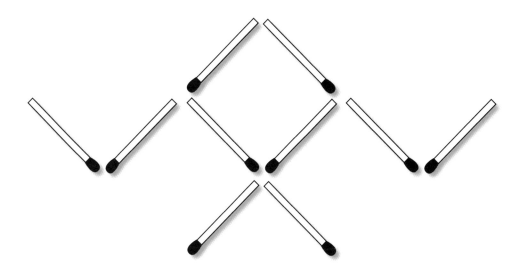

© J Dabell 2005

Move 3 matchsticks to turn the whole shape upsidedown

Matchstick dog

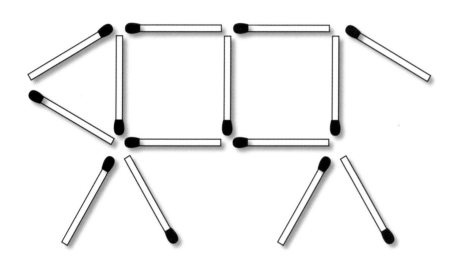

Move just 1 matchstick to change the matchstick animal's direction

Extra Question

Multiply the number of oblique lines by the number of horizontal lines.

Answer

7 x 4 = 28

Solution

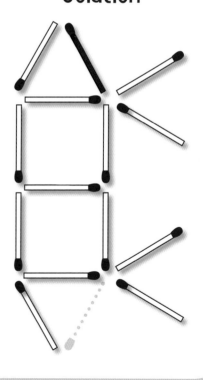

five away

Extra Question

Count the matchsticks and write out all the factors of this number.

Answer

19, the factors are 1 and 19.

Solution

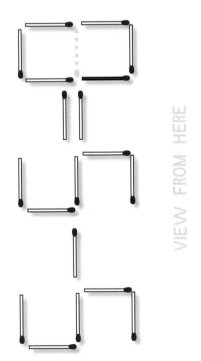

VIEW FROM HERE

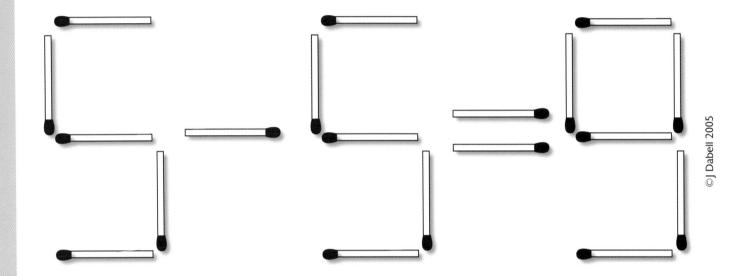

Move 1 matchstick to make this equation true

22 FOUr to one

© J Dabell 2005

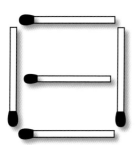  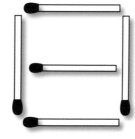

Remove 4 matchsticks to leave one

Add the number of matches to the first square number, the first cube number and the first triangular number.

Answer

15 + 1 + 1 + 1 = 18

Solution

Three, two, one?

23

Extra Question

Count the matchsticks. What shape has this number of sides?

Answer

An enneakaidecagon

Solution

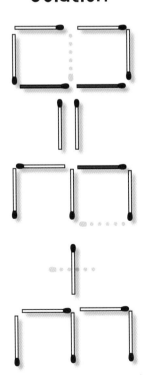

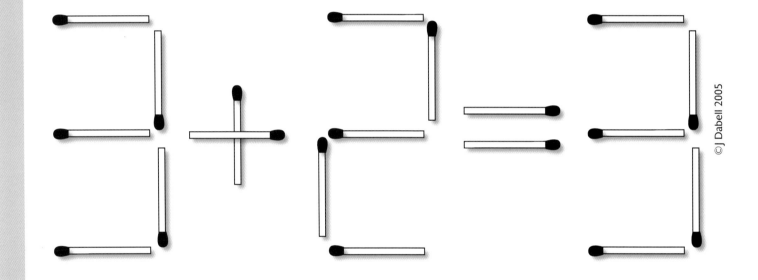

Move 3 matchsticks
to make this equation true

Lose four

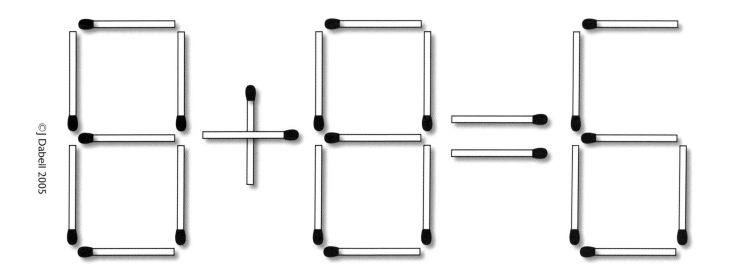

Remove 4 matchsticks to correct the equation

©J Dabell 2005

Extra Question

Subtract the total number of matches from a $\frac{1}{4}$ of ten squared.

Answer

10 squared = 100
$\frac{1}{4}$ of 100 = 25
25 - 24 = 1

Solution

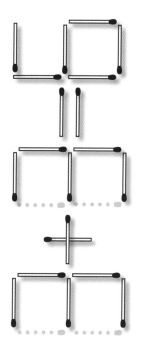

Extra Question

Multiply three by the
third prime number.

Answer

3 x 5 = 15

Solution

Tally ho!

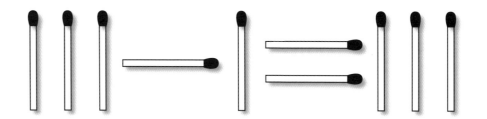

Move 1 matchstick
to correct the equation

StiCK aT it

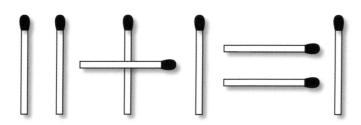

Move 1 matchstick
to correct the equation

Extra Question
Multiply the total number
of matches by the mode of
1, 2, 2, 3, 4, 5, 5, 5, 6, 7

Answer
8 x 5 = 40

Solution

© J Dabell 2005

Extra Question

Multiply the number of parallelograms you can see by the total number of matches.

Answer

There are four parallelograms (one small and one large rectangle, a square and a conventional parallelogram).
4 x 14 = 56

Solution

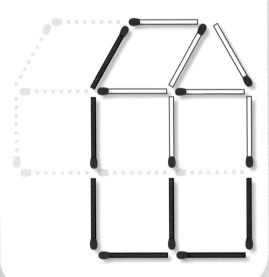

moving UP

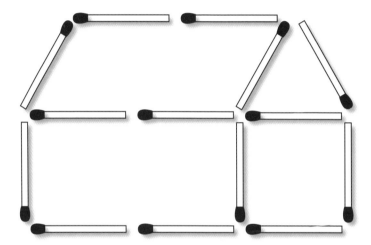

© J Dabell 2005

Move 7 matchsticks to give the house 2 levels

TRAPEZIUM

28

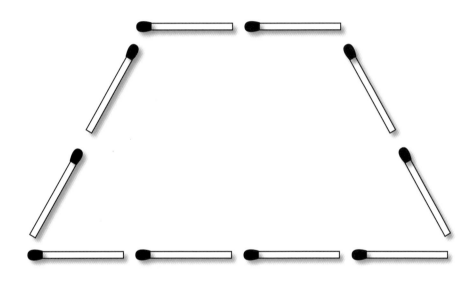

Add 5 matchsticks to make 4 congruent trapeziums

Extra Question

Add the interior angles of a trapezium to the number of acute angles found in the trapezium shown.

Answer

360 + 2 = 362

Solution

© J Dabell 2005

Extra Question

Square the number of matches then add the number of faces a cuboid has.

Answer

8 squared = 64
64 + 6 = 70

Solution

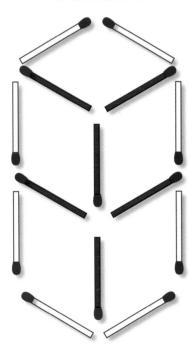

Octagon to Cuboid

29

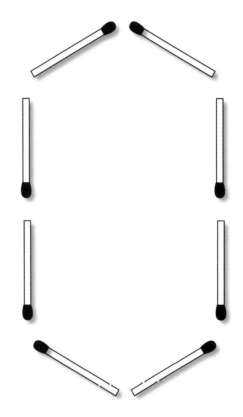

Add 6 matchsticks to form 5 equal shapes

Hexagon to parallelograms

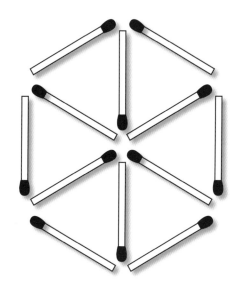

Move 3 matchsticks to make 6 equal shapes

Extra Question

Add the number of equilateral triangles to the number of exterior matches then divide by the first composite number.

Answer

6 + 6 = 12

12 ÷ 4 = 3

Solution

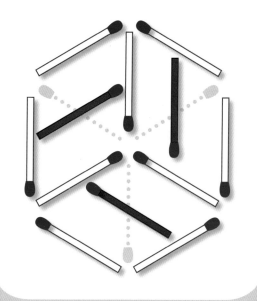

Extra Question

Is $\frac{1}{4}$ of the total number of matches greater than or less than 50% of the number of sides a dodecagon has?

Answer

$16 \div 4 = 4$

50% of 12 is 6

4 is less than 6.

Solution

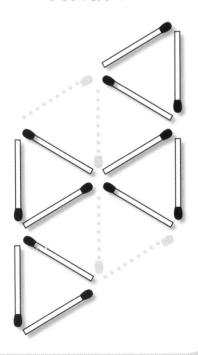

Lozenge

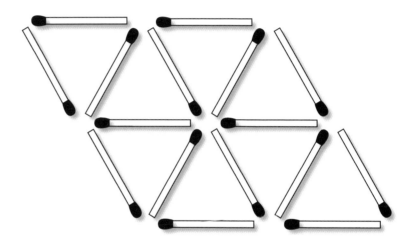

Remove 4 matchsticks to leave 4 equilateral triangles

© J Dabell 2005

32 ten to the dozen

**Move 6 matchsticks
to make a dozen**

Extra Question

Multiply the number of matches by the third factor of ten and then subtract a baker's dozen.

Answer

9 x 5 = 45
45 - 13 = 32

Solution

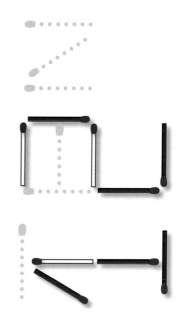

Extra Question

Subtract the number of congruent shapes from the number of matches shown.

Answer

13 - 6 = 7

Solution

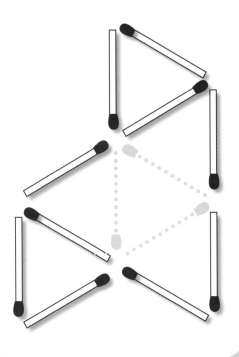

STiCKY PRObleM

33

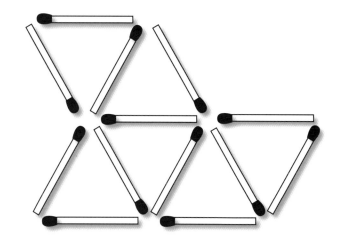

Remove 3 matchsticks to leave 3 triangles

Ladders

© J Dabell 2005

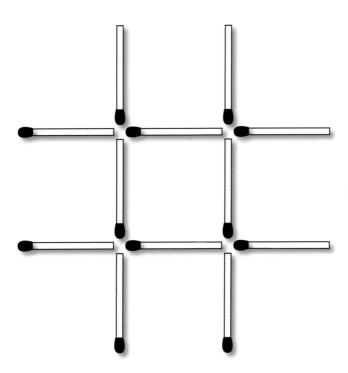

Move 3 matchsticks to leave 3 squares

Extra Question

Count the matches and then list all the factors of this number.

Answer

The number of matches = 12.
The factors of 12 are 1, 2, 3, 4, 6, 12.

Solution

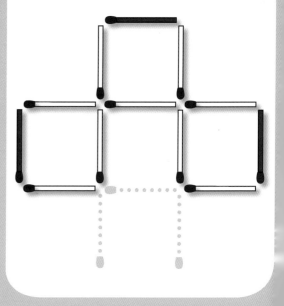

Extra Question

How many lines of
symmetry does a
square have?

Answer

4

Solution

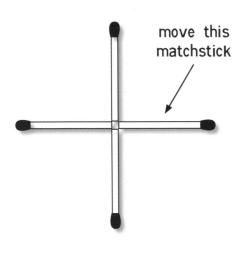

move this
matchstick

Cross move

Move 1 matchstick
to make a square

moving house

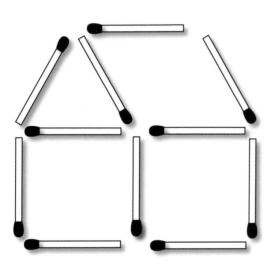

Move 1 matchstick
to make the house face the other way

Extra Question

Multiply the number of rhombuses by the total number of matches.

Answer

There are three rhombuses (the two squares and the parallelogram).
3 x 11 = 33

Solution

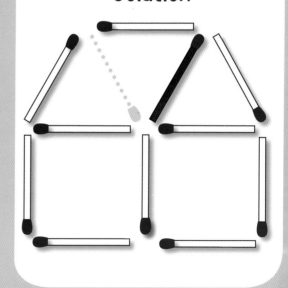

Fishy

37

Extra Question

If an octopus eats 8 fish every hour, how many fish does it eat in 720 minutes?

Answer

720 minutes is 12 hours so 12 x 8 = 96 fish.

Solution

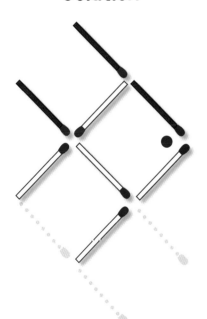

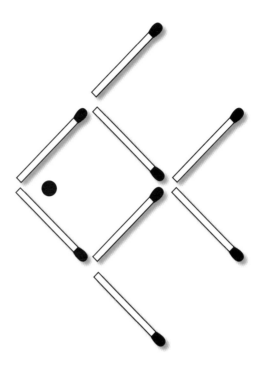

Move 3 matchsticks
to make the fish swim to the right
(you can move the eye as well)

magic

Move 2 matchsticks so that the coin is outside the glass

Extra Question

Divide the number of ten pence pieces in £46.00 by the total number of matches.

Answer

$460 \div 4 = 115$

Solution

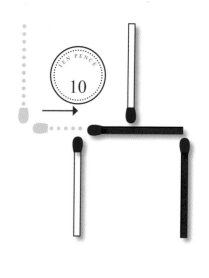

Extra Question

Take 19 from 100 and then multiply your answer by 9.

Answer

100 - 19 = 81
81 x 9 = 729

Solution

Five to nine

Add 5 matchsticks to make nine

40

Shape Shifter

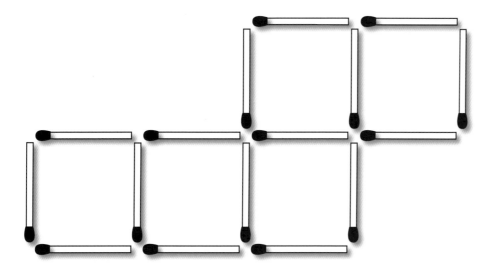

Move 2 matchsticks to make 4 squares

Extra Question

Write the total number of matches in Roman numerals.

Answer

XVI

Solution

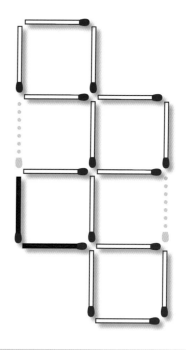

© J Dabell 2005

Extra Question

What is the next perfect square after 4?

Answer

9, 3 x 3

Solution

Perfect square

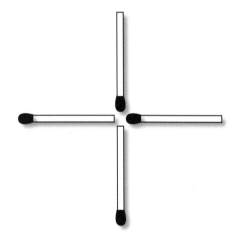

Move 1 matchstick to make a square

42 square fun

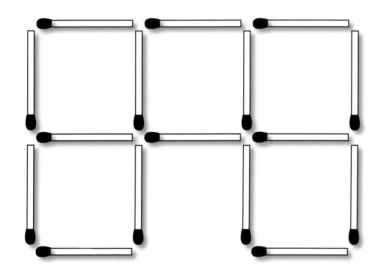

Move 3 matchsticks to get 4 squares

Extra Question

Find the circumference of the shape and times this number by the number of interior matches.

Answer

12 matches make the circumference (perimeter).
12 x 4 = 48

Solution

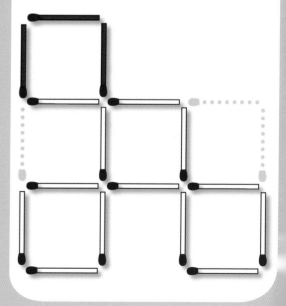

Extra Question

Is the number of matches shown greater than or less than $\frac{1}{4}$ of a score?

Answer

A quarter of a score is
20 ÷ 4 = 5,
there are 9 matchsticks
so the answer is
greater than.

Solution

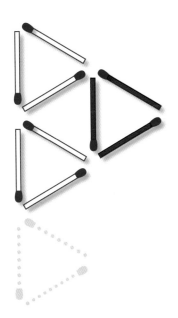

Tri-five

Move 3 matchsticks to make 5 triangles

Triangular Magic

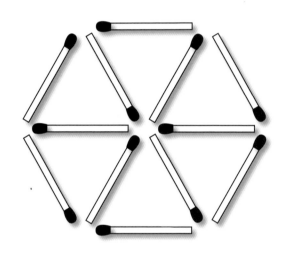

Move 4 matchsticks to make 3 equilateral triangles

Extra Question

Multiply the number of horizontal lines by the number of oblique lines.

Answer

4 x 8 = 32

Solution

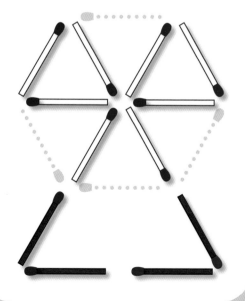

Extra Question

Add the number of squares you can see to the second composite number.

Answer

There are five squares, which added to 6, the second composite number, gives 11.

Solution

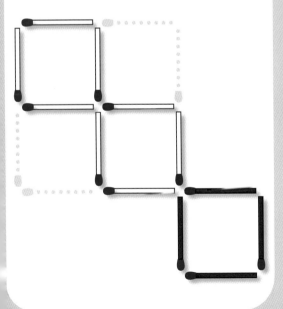

FOUr into three

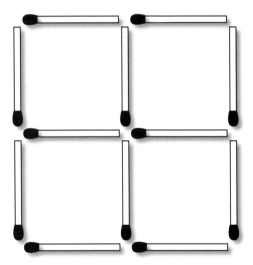

© J Dabell 2005

Move 4 matchsticks to make 3 squares

46 Tetra-trigon

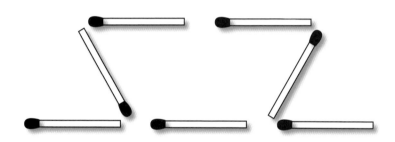

Move 2 matchsticks to make 1 rhombus and 1 equilateral triangle

Extra Question

Square the number of matches then subtract this from 1000.

Answer

7 x 7 = 49

1000 - 49 = 951

Solution

Extra Question

Count the number of matches and add this to the time you have made. How many more minutes will it be to midnight?

Answer

It is five hours and 24 minutes to midnight which is 324 minutes.

Solution

VIEW FROM HERE

Set the CIOCK

© J Dabell 2005

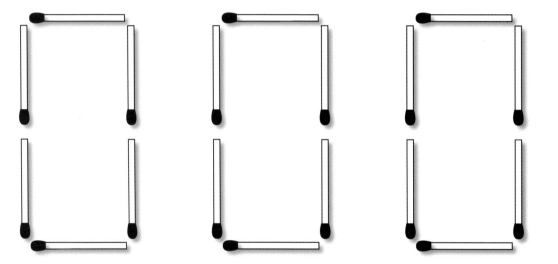

Move 4 matchsticks
to set the clock to 18 minutes past 6

Quadforce

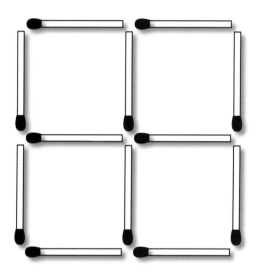

Move 2 matchsticks
to make 3 squares
and another 6 rectangles

Extra Question

How many degrees are there in 4 squares?

Answer

360 x 4 = 1440 degrees

Solution

Extra Question

How many lines of reflective symmetry does the letter L have and what is its order of rotational symmetry?

Answer

It has one line of reflective symmetry and order of rotation of 1.

Solution

L of a rotation

49

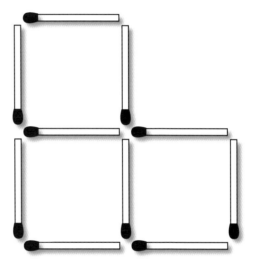

Move 2 matchsticks to turn the L shape upside down

50 square flair

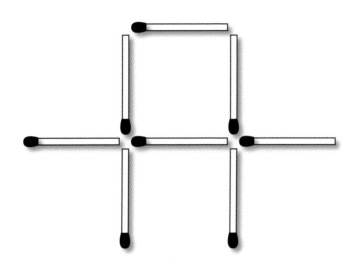

Move 2 matchsticks to make 2 squares

Extra Question

Multiply the number of matches by the fifth prime number giving your answer in Roman numerals.

Answer

8 x 11 = 88
LXXXVIII

Solution

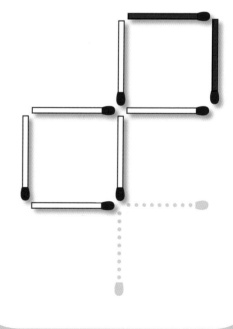

Tri-quads

Extra Question

The total number of matches is greater than the fourth composite number.
True or false?

Answer

True because the fourth composite number is 9.

Solution

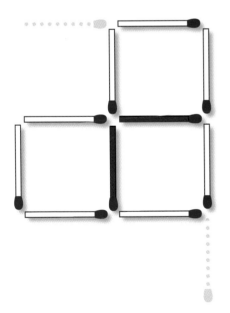

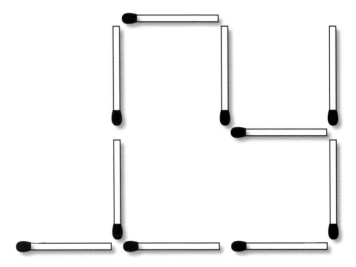

Move 2 matchsticks to make 3 squares

© J Dabell 2005

52 Tally folly

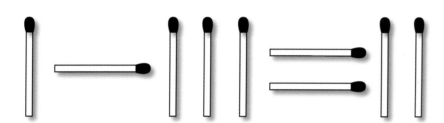

Move only 1 matchstick to make this equation true

Extra Question

The total number of matches is smaller than the fourth triangular number.
True or false?

Answer

True because the fourth triangular number is 10 and there are 9 matches.

Solution

Extra Question

Quintuple the total number of matches.

Answer

5 x 7 = 35

Solution

square tally

53

Move 4 matchsticks to make 2 squares

square move

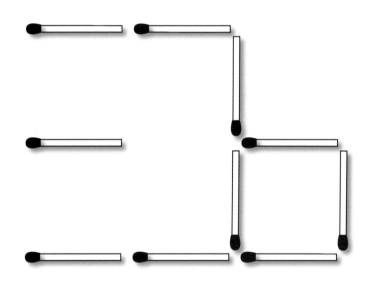

Move 3 matchsticks to make 2 squares

Extra Question

Divide the number of vertical matches by 2.

Answer

3 ÷ 2 = 1.5

Solution

54

Extra Question

If the Roman numeral for 10 is X, how would you write 50?

Answer

L or X X X X X

Solution

ROaming numerals

55

© J Dabell 2005

Move 2 matchsticks to make this equation true

WINDOW SQUARES

© J Dabell 2005

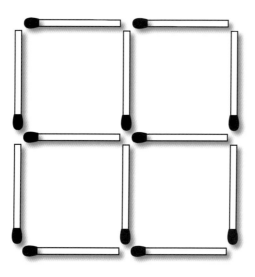

Move 4 matchsticks to make 10 squares

Extra Question

What other names can you think of for a square?

Answer

A square is also a parallelogram, a polygon, a quadrilateral, a rectangle, a rhombus, and a tetragon.

Solution

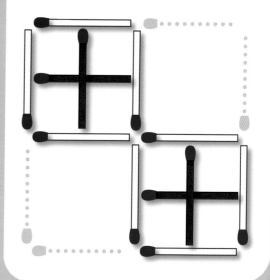

Extra Question

How many oblique lines make up the number 5 when written in tally form?

Answer

One, as it is the bar that crosses the gate.

Solution

five to two 57

© J Dabell 2005

Remove 2 matchsticks to make this equation true

Congruent Oblongs

© J Dabell 2005

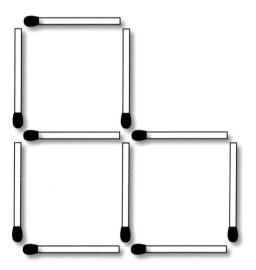

Move 2 matchsticks to make 4 identical rectangles

Extra Question

If three squares make 12, what do six septagons make?

Answer

3 x 4
(number of sides a square has) = 12
so 6 x 7
(the number of sides a septagon has) = 42

Solution

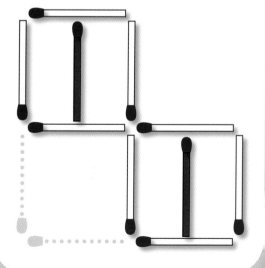

Extra Question

Count the number of tetragons and multiply this by $\frac{1}{5}$ of the total number of matches.

Answer

There are three tetragons (the oblongs).
$\frac{1}{5}$ of 15 = 3
3 x 3 = 9

Solution

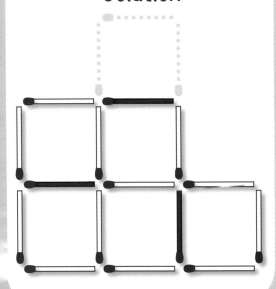

Oblongs to squares

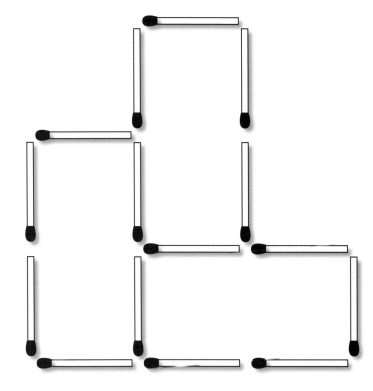

Move 3 matchsticks to make 6 squares

Eight into two

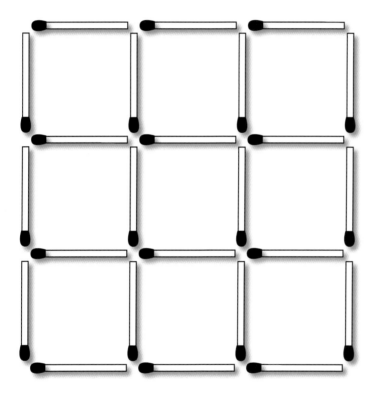

Remove 8 matchsticks to make 2 squares

Extra Question

Count the total number of matches and work out how many times they will go into a gross.

Answer

There are 24 matches.

144 (a gross) ÷ 24 = 6

Solution

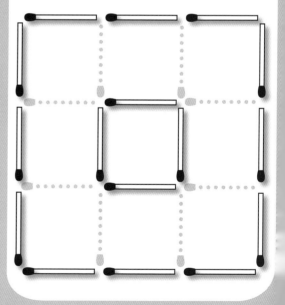

© J Dabell 2005

Extra Question

What is the next prime number after you subtract 7 from the total number of matches?

Answer

24 - 7 = 17
The next prime number after 17 is 19.

Solution

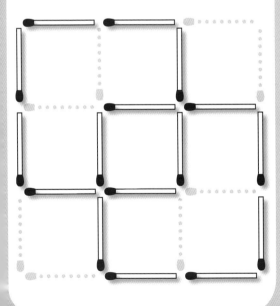

Eight into three

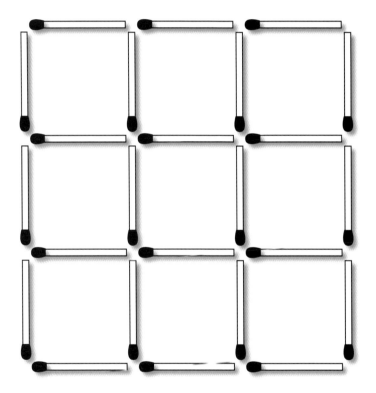

© J Dabell 2005

Remove 8 matchsticks to make 3 squares

Eight into four

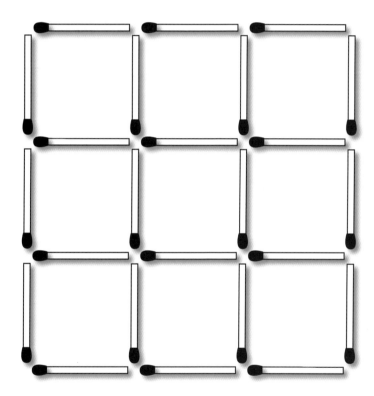

Remove 8 matchsticks to leave 4 squares

Extra Question

If each matchstick measures 34mm, how many cm would the interior matches make if they were laid end to end?

Answer

34cm x 12 = 40.8cm

Solution

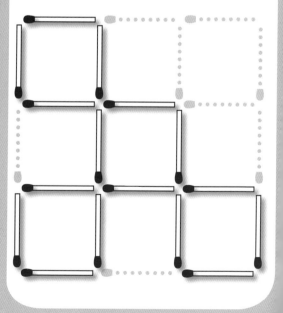

Extra Question

Divide the total number of matches by the number of matches that make up the perimeter.

Answer

40 ÷ 16 = 2.5

Solution

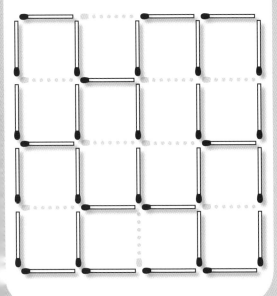

TWO SCORE

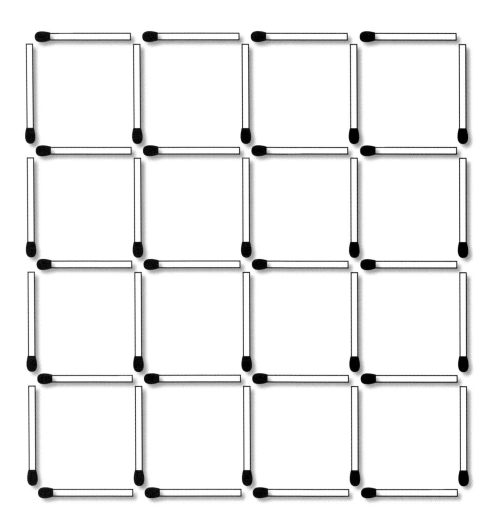

What is the smallest number of matchsticks you can remove to leave no squares?

five alive

© J Dabell 2005

Move 1 matchstick
to make this equation true

Extra Question

Divide the number of oblique matches by the rest and express your answer as a fraction.

Answer

There are 4 oblique lines which divided by 6 makes $^2/_3$.

Solution

Extra Question

Count the matchsticks and write the 8th multiple of the total number.

Answer

8 x 12 = 96

Solution

Matchstick Maths

649

© J Dabell 2005

Move 1 matchstick to make this equation true

66 Match Spiral

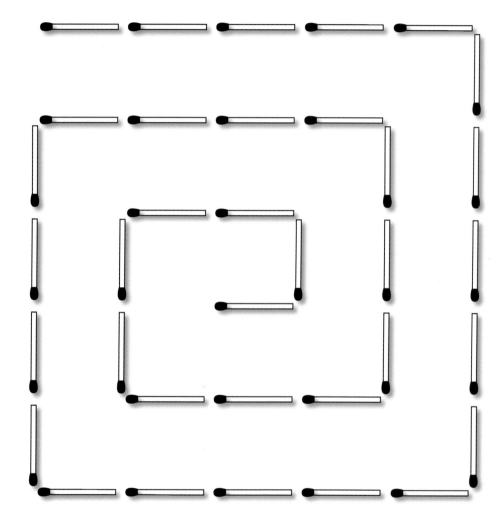

© J Dabell 2005

Move 4 matchsticks to make 3 squares

Extra Question

Find the total number of matches and write down the factors of this number.

Answer

There are 35 matches. The factors of 35 are 1, 5, 7, 35.

Solution

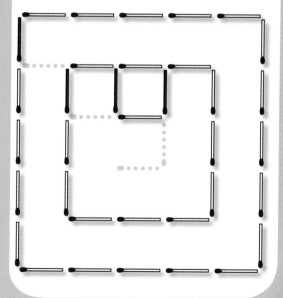

notes

notes